TODAY'S HITS
Playalong *for* Violin

WISE PUBLICATIONS
London/New York/Paris/Sydney/Copenhagen/Madrid/Tokyo

Exclusive Distributors:
Music Sales Limited
8/9 Frith Street, London W1D 3JB, England.
Music Sales Pty Limited
120 Rothschild Avenue, Rosebery, NSW 2018, Australia.

Order No. AM966042
ISBN 0-7119-8364-X
This book © Copyright 2001 by Wise Publications.

Music arranged by Simon Lesley.
Music processed by Enigma Music Production Services.
Cover photography by George Taylor.
Printed in the United Kingdom by Page Bros., Norwich, Norfolk.

CD produced by Jonas Perrson.
Instrumental solos by Dermot Crehan.

Your Guarantee of Quality:
As publishers, we strive to produce every book to
the highest commercial standards.
The music has been freshly engraved and the book has been
carefully designed to minimise awkward page turns and
to make playing from it a real pleasure.
Particular care has been given to specifying acid-free, neutral-sized
paper made from pulps which have not been elemental chlorine bleached.
This pulp is from farmed sustainable forests and was
produced with special regard for the environment.
Throughout, the printing and binding have been planned to
ensure a sturdy, attractive publication which should give years of enjoyment.
If your copy fails to meet our high standards,
please inform us and we will gladly replace it.

Music Sales' complete catalogue describes thousands of
titles and is available in full colour sections by subject,
direct from Music Sales Limited.
Please state your areas of interest and send a
cheque/postal order for £1.50 for postage to:
Music Sales Limited, Newmarket Road, Bury St. Edmunds, Suffolk IP33 3YB.

www.musicsales.com

Eternal Flame

Words & Music by Billy Steinberg, Tom Kelly & Susanna Hoffs

7

Let Love Be Your Energy

Words & Music by Robbie Williams & Guy Chambers

Don't Stop Movin'

Words & Music by Simon Ellis, Sheppard Solomon & S Club 7

Happy groovy ♩ = 116

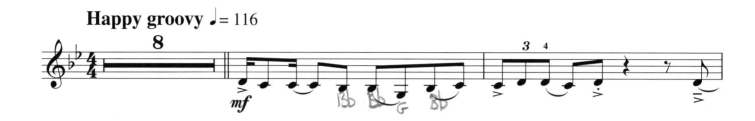

11

quasi improvised solo

non legato

sub. **ff**

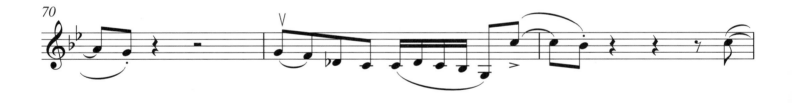

pizz.

mp

Out Of Reach

Words & Music by Gabrielle & Jonathan Shorten

Only For A While

Words & Music by Joseph Washbourn

Indie-rock ballad ♩= 68

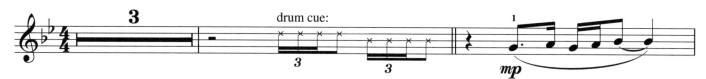

Run For Cover

Words & Music by Cameron McVey, Johnny Lipsey, Paul Simm, Siobhan Donaghy, Keisha Buchanan & Mutya Buena

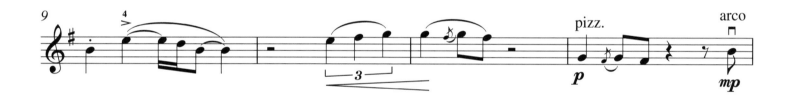

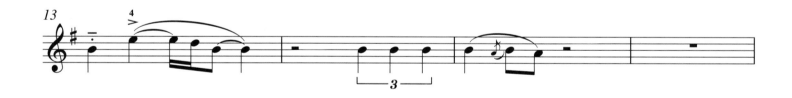

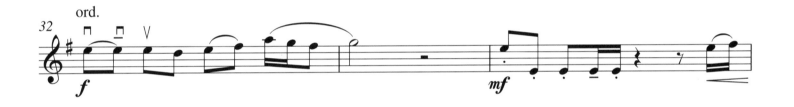

Sail Away

Words & Music by David Gray

2 bar click count in.

Dreaming and moody, with lazy ♪'s ♩ = 67

mp legato e cantabile

like waves

Sing

Words & Music by Fran Healy

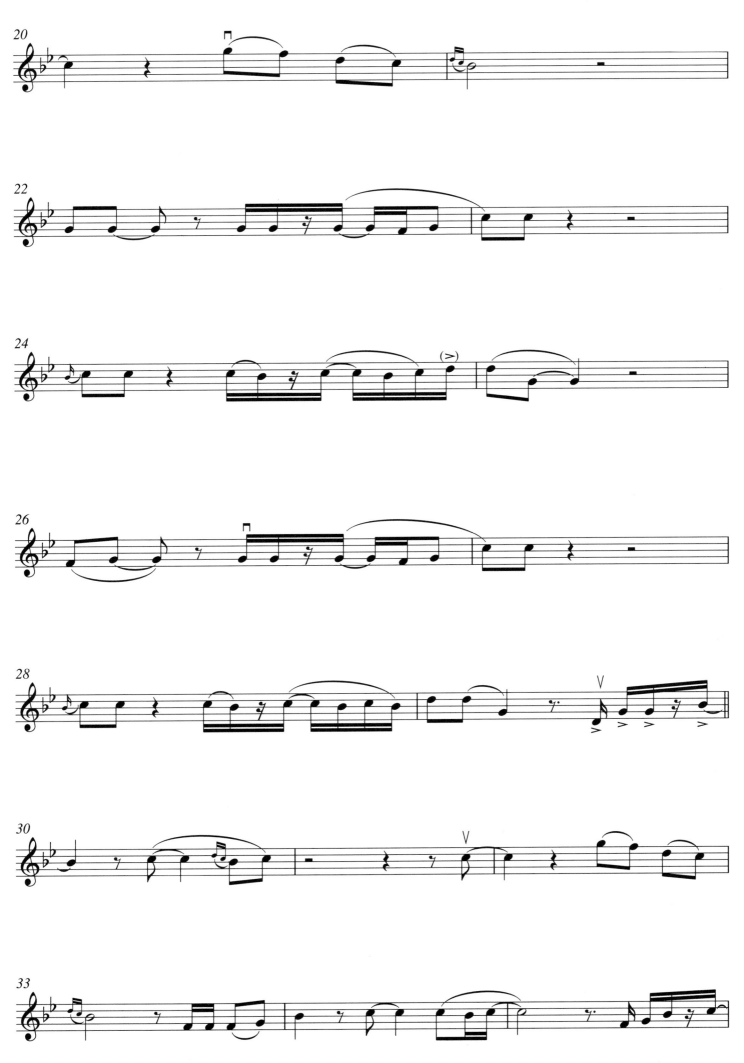

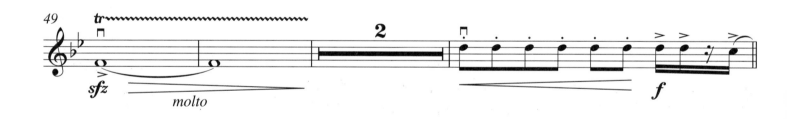

Pure And Simple

Words & Music by Tim Hawes, Pete Kirtley & Alison Clarkson

What Took You So Long?

Words & Music by Emma Bunton, Richard Stannard, Julian Gallagher, Martin Harrington, John Themis & Dave Morgan